100 GRADED VIOLIN SOLOS

100
GRADED
VIOLIN
SOLOS

WISE PUBLICATIONS
part of The Music Sales Group

London / New York / Paris / Sydney / Copenhagen / Berlin / Madrid / Tokyo

Published by
Wise Publications
14-15 Berners Street, London W1T 3LJ, UK.

Exclusive Distributors:
Music Sales Limited
Distribution Centre, Newmarket Road,
Bury St Edmunds, Suffolk IP33 3YB, UK.
Music Sales Pty Limited
20 Resolution Drive, Caringbah, NSW 2229, Australia.

Order No. AM992156
ISBN 978-1-84772-367-3
This book © Copyright 2007 Wise Publications,
a division of Music Sales Limited.

Edited by Jessica Williams.
Music processed by Paul Ewers Music Design.
Cover design by Michael Bell Design.
Printed in the EU.

Your Guarantee of Quality
As publishers, we strive to produce every book to
the highest commercial standards.
This book has been carefully designed to minimise awkward
page turns and to make playing from it a real pleasure.
Particular care has been given to specifying acid-free, neutral-sized
paper made from pulps which have not been elemental chlorine bleached.
This pulp is from farmed sustainable forests and
was produced with special regard for the environment.
Throughout, the printing and binding have been planned to ensure
a sturdy, attractive publication which should give years of enjoyment.
If your copy fails to meet our high standards,
please inform us and we will gladly replace it.

www.musicsales.com

GRADING NOTES

The pieces in this book have been carefully graded according to
various criteria such as rhythmic complexity, phrasing, tempo, key, range, etc.
Look for the number of stars for each piece to give you
an idea of the approximate playing level.
All musicians have particular strengths and weaknesses,
so the grading offered here should be taken as a suggestion only.

Generally, pieces with one star have simple rhythms,
straight forward phrasings and few difficult intervals;
essentially diatonic and in easier keys.

Pieces with two stars will have more challenging passages,
perhaps containing more rhythmic complexity,
more advanced key signatures and possibly explore a wider
range on the intrument.

Three-star pieces may include chromaticism,
challenging articulation and more advanced positioning.
Read through rhythms and keys before playing, and check for
time-signature changes and correct phrasing.

Angels

Words & Music by Robbie Williams & Guy Chambers

Angie

Words & Music by Mick Jagger & Keith Richards

Beautiful

Words & Music by Linda Perry

Any Dream Will Do
(from 'Joseph And The Amazing Technicolor® Dreamcoat')

Music by Andrew Lloyd Webber
Lyrics by Tim Rice

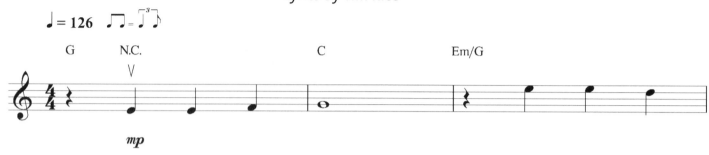

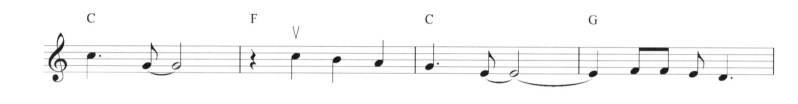

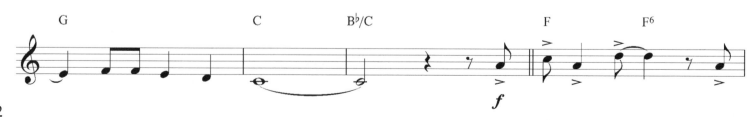

12

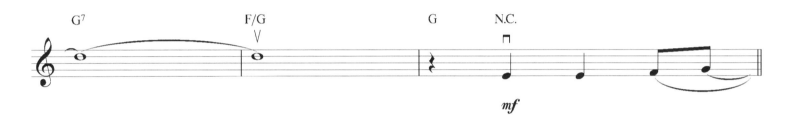

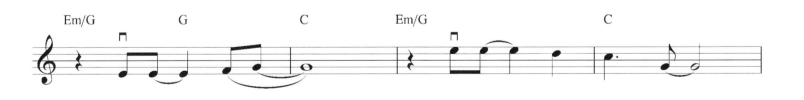

...Baby One More Time

Words & Music by Max Martin

14

Beautiful Stranger

Words & Music by Madonna & William Orbit

The Best

Words & Music by Mike Chapman & Holly Knight

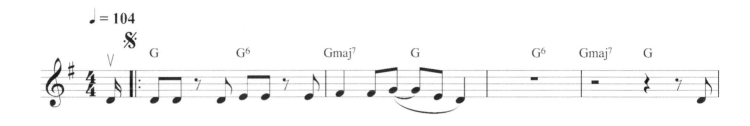

Big Spender

Words by Dorothy Fields
Music by Cy Coleman

Moderate Swing

20

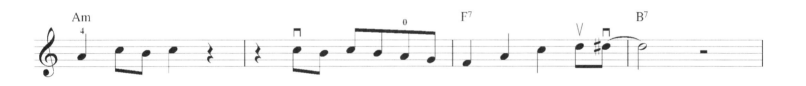

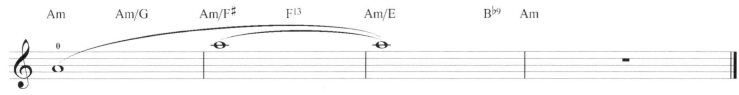

Born Free

Words by Don Black
Music by John Barry

Born To Try

Words & Music by Delta Goodrem & Audius Mtawarira

23

Bridge Over Troubled Water

Words & Music by Paul Simon

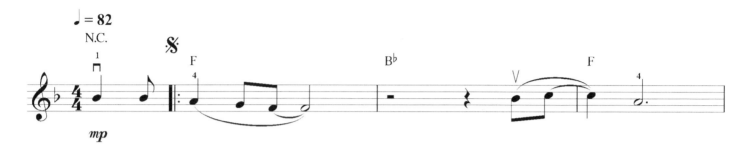

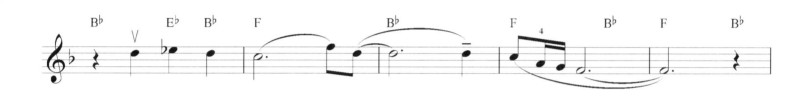

24

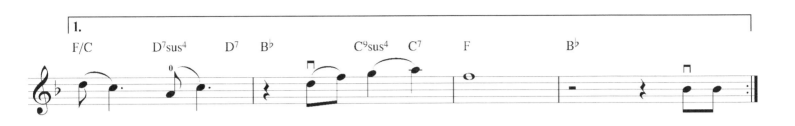

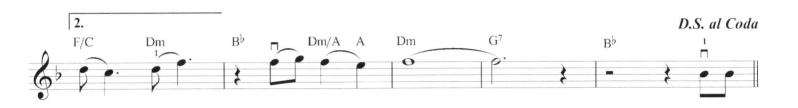

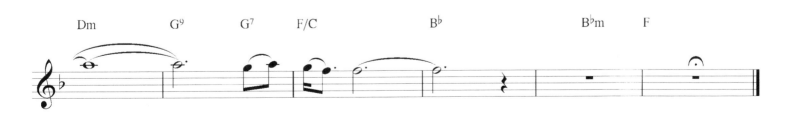

Can You Feel The Love Tonight
(from 'The Lion King')

Words by Tim Rice
Music by Elton John

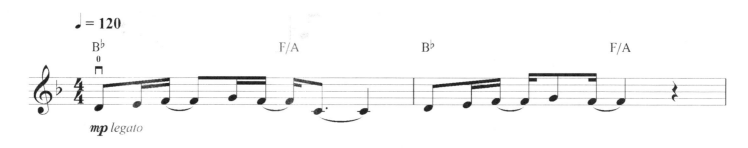

Brown Eyed Girl

Words & Music by Van Morrison

Can't Get You Out Of My Head

Words & Music by Cathy Dennis & Rob Davis

Can't Help Falling In Love

Words & Music by George David Weiss, Hugo Peretti & Luigi Creatore

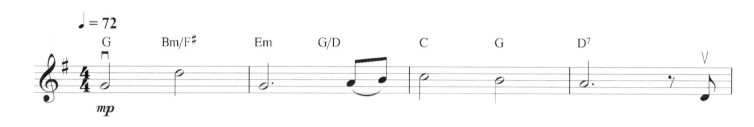

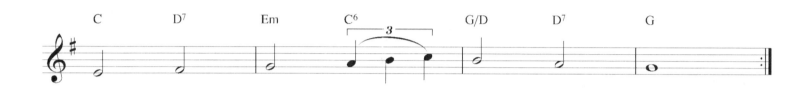

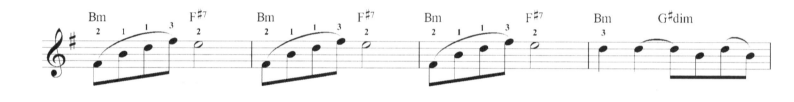

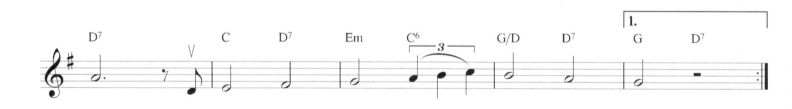

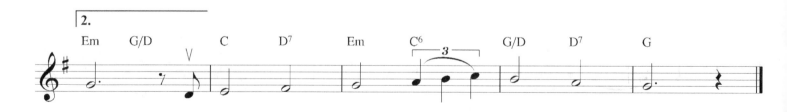

Clocks

Words & Music by Guy Berryman, Chris Martin, Jon Buckland & Will Champion

Crazy

Words & Music by Thomas Callaway, Brian Burton, Gianfranco Reverberi & Gian Piero Reverberi

Cry Me A River

Words & Music by Justin Timberlake, Scott Storch & Tim Mosley

Don't Cry For Me Argentina

(from 'Evita')

Music by Andrew Lloyd Webber
Lyrics by Tim Rice

Don't Get Around Much Anymore

Words by Bob Russell
Music by Duke Ellington

Don't Know Why

Words & Music by Jesse Harris

Don't Look Back In Anger

Words & Music by Noel Gallagher

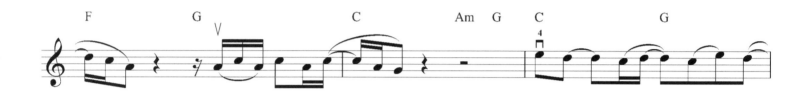

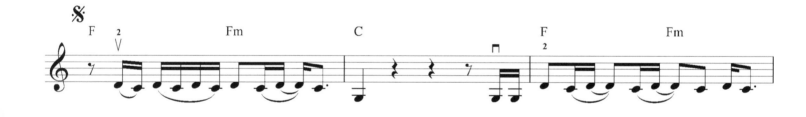

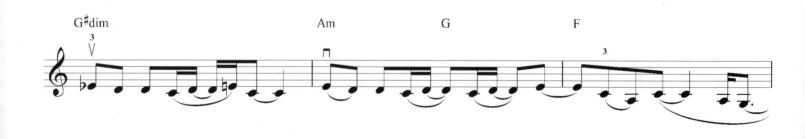

(Everything I Do) I Do It For You

Words by Bryan Adams & Robert John Lange
Music by Michael Kamen

Fairytale Of New York

Words & Music by Shane MacGowan & Jem Finer

41

Feeling Good

Words & Music by Leslie Bricusse & Anthony Newley

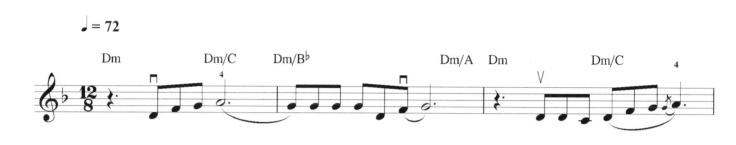

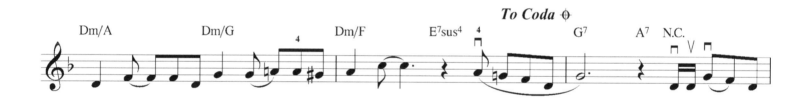

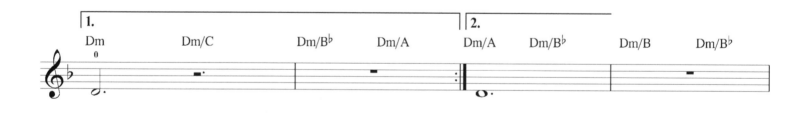

D.C. al Coda

Fever

Words & Music by John Davenport & Eddie Cooley

Moderate jump beat

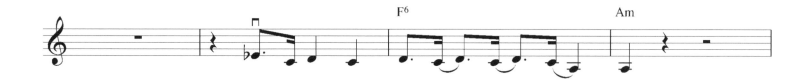

Fields Of Gold

Words & Music by Sting

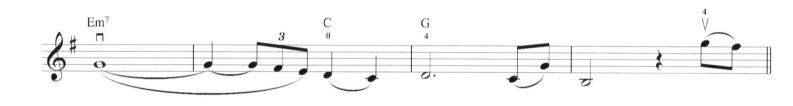

Fly Me To The Moon
(In Other Words)

Words & Music by Bart Howard

Fix You

Words & Music by Guy Berryman, Chris Martin, Jon Buckland & Will Champion

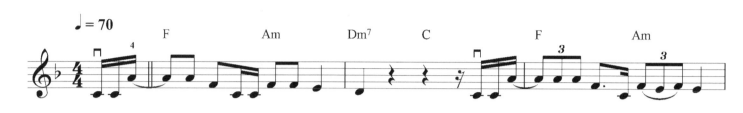

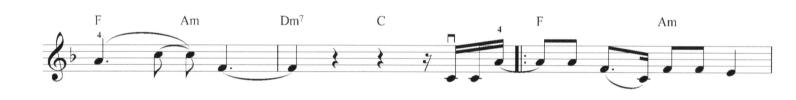

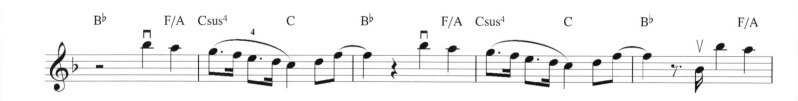

Girl, You'll Be A Woman Soon

Words & Music by Neil Diamond

The Godfather (Love Theme)

Music by Nino Rota

Gold

Words & Music by Prince

Goldfinger

Words by Leslie Bricusse & Anthony Newley
Music by John Barry

Golden Touch

Words & Music by Johnny Borrell

54

Gravity

Words & Music by Guy Berryman, Chris Martin, Jon Buckland & Will Champion

Hero

Words & Music by Enrique Iglesias, Paul Barry & Mark Taylor

Hallelujah

Words & Music by Leonard Cohen

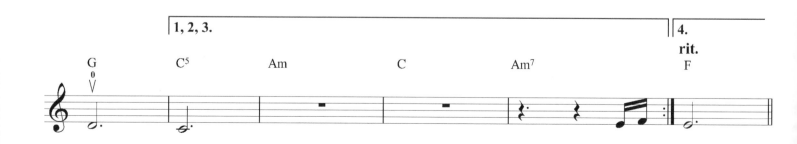

58

Heaven

Words & Music by Bryan Adams & Jim Vallance

Hey Jude

Words & Music by John Lennon & Paul McCartney

I Get The Sweetest Feeling

Words & Music by Van McCoy & Alicia Evelyn

I Got You (I Feel Good)

Words & Music by James Brown

I Will Always Love You

Words & Music by Dolly Parton

Imagine

Words & Music by John Lennon

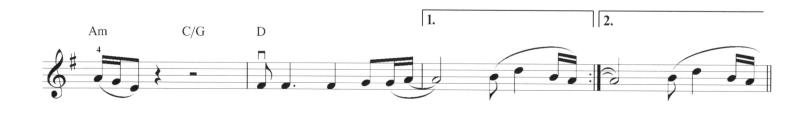

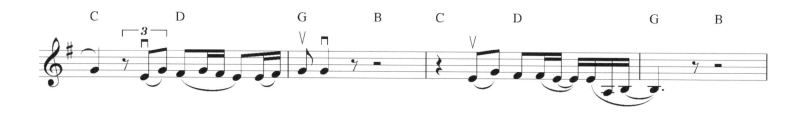

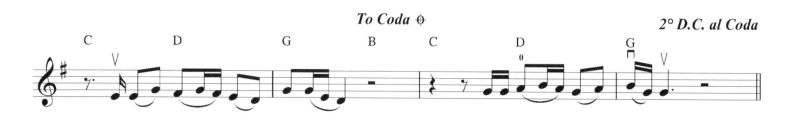

Is It Any Wonder?

Words & Music by Richard Hughes, James Sanger, Tim Rice-Oxley & Tom Chaplin

Ironic

Words by Alanis Morissette
Music by Alanis Morissette & Glen Ballard

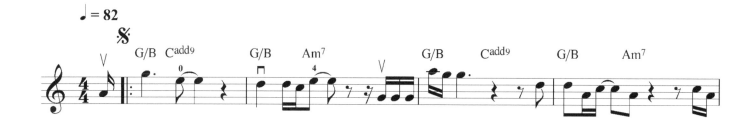

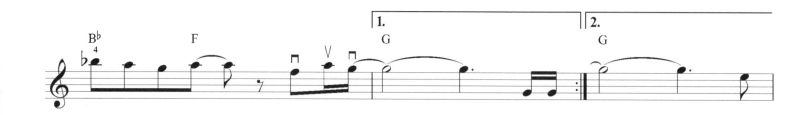

D.S. al Coda   ⊕ *Coda*

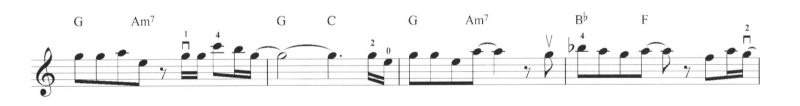

Israelites

Words & Music by Desmond Dacres & Leslie Kong

Knockin' On Heaven's Door

Words & Music by Bob Dylan

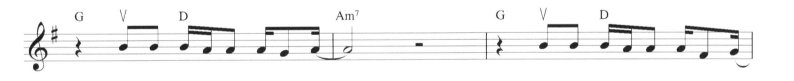

It's Not Unusual

Words & Music by Gordon Mills & Les Reed

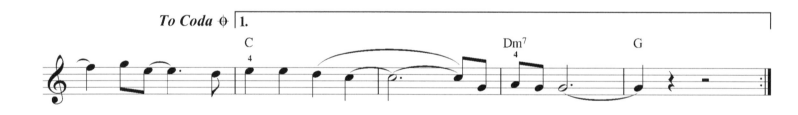

D.C. al Coda

Fade to end

Just The Way I'm Feeling

Words & Music by Grant Nicholas

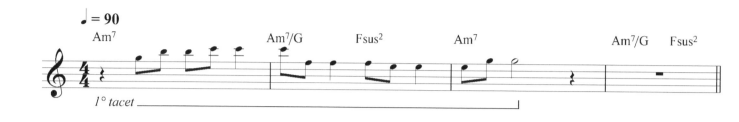

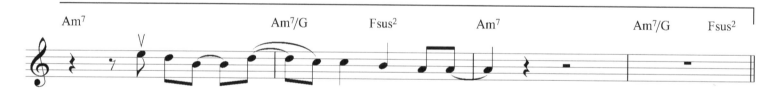

The Lady In Red

Words & Music by Chris de Burgh

77

Leave Right Now

Words & Music by Francis White

Let It Be

Words & Music by John Lennon & Paul McCartney

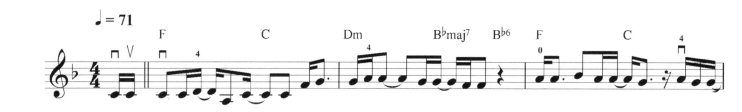

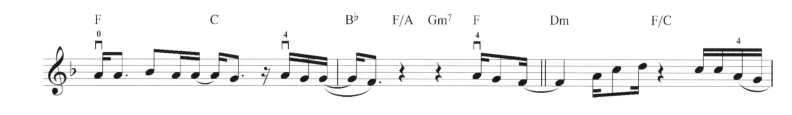

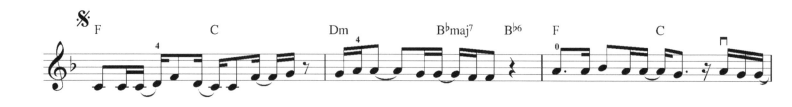

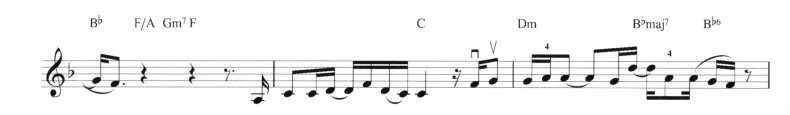

To Coda ⊕

D.S. al Coda

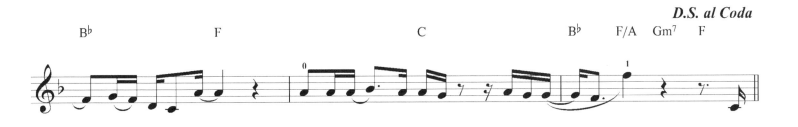

⊕ *Coda*

rall.

Like A Virgin

Words & Music by Billy Steinberg & Tom Kelly

Lover Man
(Oh Where Can You Be)

Words & Music by Jimmy Davis, Roger Ramirez & Jimmy Sherman

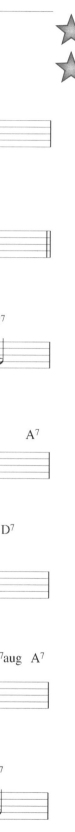

Livin' On A Prayer

Words & Music by Richie Sambora, Desmond Child & Jon Bon Jovi

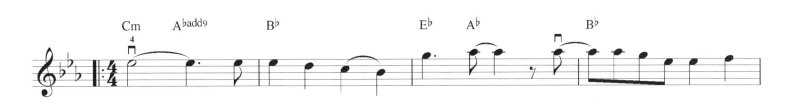

Lovin' You

Words & Music by Minnie Riperton & Richard Rudolph

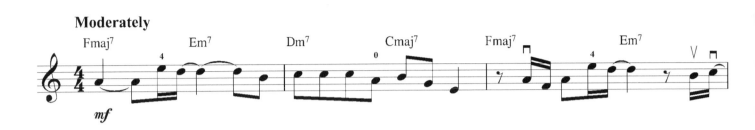

D.S. al Coda

✛ *Coda*

Repeat to fade

Memory
(from 'Cats')

Music by Andrew Lloyd Webber
Text by Trevor Nunn after T.S. Eliot

89

Mad World

Words & Music by Roland Orzabal

Missing

Words by Tracey Thorn
Music by Ben Watt

Mission: Impossible

Music by Lalo Schifrin

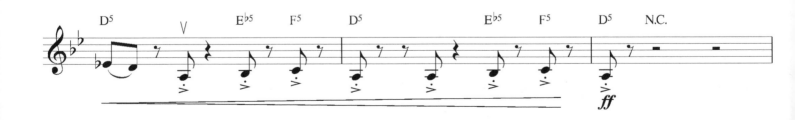

92

The Model

Words & Music by Ralf Hutter, Karl Bartos & Emil Schult

Moon River

Words by Johnny Mercer
Music by Henry Mancini

Mrs. Robinson

Words & Music by Paul Simon

Nothing In My Way

Words & Music by Richard Hughes, James Sanger, Tim Rice-Oxley & Tom Chaplin

Oh Yeah (On The Radio)

Words & Music by Bryan Ferry

98

To Coda ⊕

D.C. al Coda

⊕ *Coda*

One

Words & Music by David Evans, Adam Clayton, Paul Hewson & Laurence Mullen

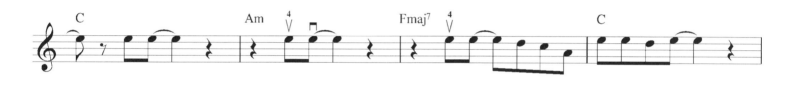

Other Side Of The World

Words & Music by KT Tunstall & Martin Terefe

102

Orange Coloured Sky

Words & Music by Milton DeLugg & Willie Stein

Penny Lane

Words & Music by John Lennon & Paul McCartney

Perfect

Words & Music by Mark E. Nevin

The Power Of Love

Words & Music by Holly Johnson, Mark O'Toole, Peter Gill & Brian Nash

Put Your Records On

Words & Music by John Beck, Steven Chrisanthou & Corinne Bailey Rae

Sail Away

Words & Music by David Gray

Run

Words & Music by Gary Lightbody, Jonathan Quinn, Mark McClelland, Nathan Connolly & Iain Archer

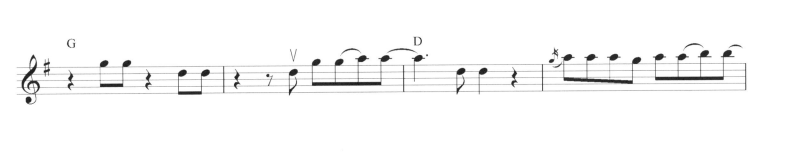

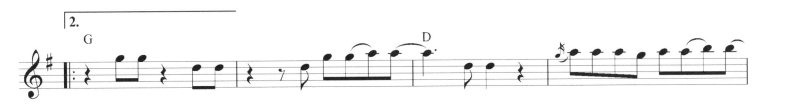

She Moves In Her Own Way

Words & Music by Luke Pritchard, Hugh Harris, Max Rafferty & Paul Garred

She's Not There

Words & Music by Rod Argent

She's The One

Words & Music by Karl Wallinger

Somebody Told Me

Words & Music by Brandon Flowers, Dave Keuning, Mark Stoermer & Ronnie Van Nucci

Son Of A Preacher Man

Words & Music by John Hurley & Ronnie Wilkins

(Sittin' On) The Dock Of The Bay

Words & Music by Steve Cropper & Otis Redding

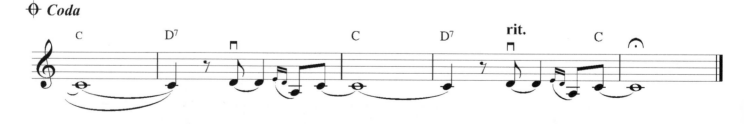

Stand By Me

Words & Music by Ben E. King, Jerry Leiber & Mike Stoller

Strangers In The Night

Words by Charles Singleton & Eddie Snyder
Music by Bert Kaempfert

Sweet Caroline

Words & Music by Neil Diamond

'Tain't What You Do
(It's The Way That Cha Do It)

Words & Music by Sy Oliver & James Young

Tainted Love

Words & Music by Ed Cobb

Take Me To The River

Words & Music by Al Green & Mabon Hodges

Tears In Heaven

Words & Music by Eric Clapton & Will Jennings

The Song From Moulin Rouge
(Where Is Your Heart)

Words by William Engvick
Music by Georges Auric

True Faith

Words & Music by Peter Hook, Stephen Hague, Bernard Sumner, Gillian Gilbert & Stephen Morris

Unchained Melody

Words by Hy Zaret
Music by Alex North

Video Killed The Radio Star

Words & Music by Geoffrey Downes, Trevor Horn & Bruce Woolley

Waterloo

Words & Music by Benny Andersson, Stig Anderson & Björn Ulvaeus

The Way You Look Tonight

Words by Dorothy Fields
Music by Jerome Kern

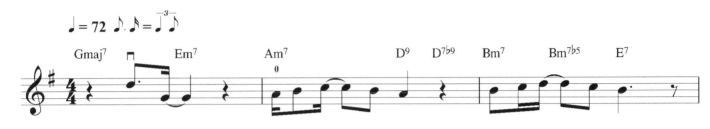
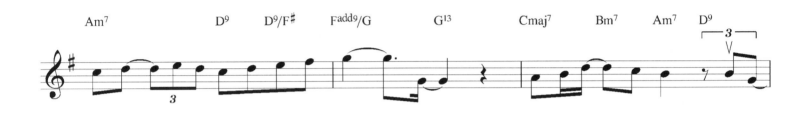

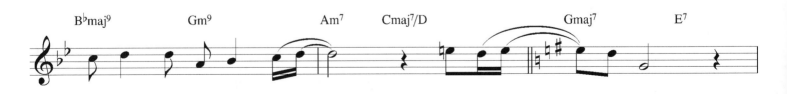

What A Wonderful World

Words & Music by George Weiss & Bob Thiele

Yellow

Words & Music by Guy Berryman, Jon Buckland, Will Champion & Chris Martin

Wonderwall

Words & Music by Noel Gallagher

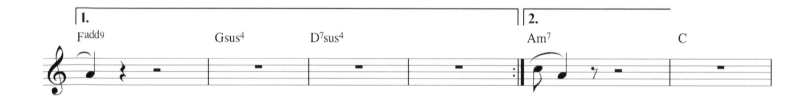

Yesterday

Words & Music by John Lennon & Paul McCartney

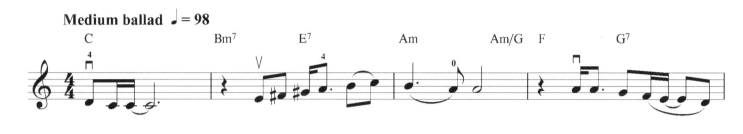

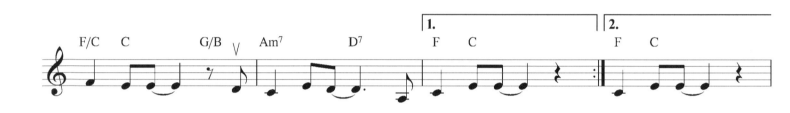

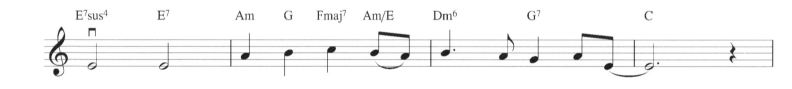

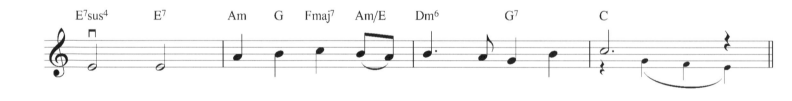

Your Song

Words & Music by Elton John & Bernie Taupin

You're Beautiful

Words & Music by Sacha Skarbek, James Blunt & Amanda Ghost

You're The One That I Want

Words & Music by John Farrar

08/12   (184223)